My Memories

A WRITTEN RECORD
OF MY LIFE AND TIMES TO HAND
DOWN TO MY FAMILY

THE
METROPOLITAN
MUSEUM
OF
ART

QUILLMARK

The illustrations in this book are by the French artist Maurice
Boutet de Monvel, who was born in Orléans in 1851 and died in
Paris in 1913. The reproductions have been selected from *Vieilles
chansons et rondes pour les petits enfants,* an album of French
children's songs, which was published in Paris in 1927. *Vieilles
chansons et rondes pour les petits enfants* is in the collection of
The Metropolitan Museum of Art, gift of Mrs. John S. Lamont, 1974.

Copyright © 1984 by The Metropolitan Museum of Art
All rights reserved
Produced by the Department of Special Publications, The Metropolitan
Museum of Art
Designed by Marleen Adlerblum
Printed and bound by Dai Nippon Printing Co., Ltd., Tokyo, Japan
ISBN 0-87099-388-7 The Metropolitan Museum of Art
ISBN 866-81861-8 Quillmark

THE AUTHOR OF THIS BOOK

Recent photograph of me

My full name: _____

This is the year: _____

All my past life is mine no more;
The trying hours are gone,
Like transitory dreams given o'er
Whose images are kept in store
By memory alone.
JOHN WILMOT, EARL OF ROCHESTER

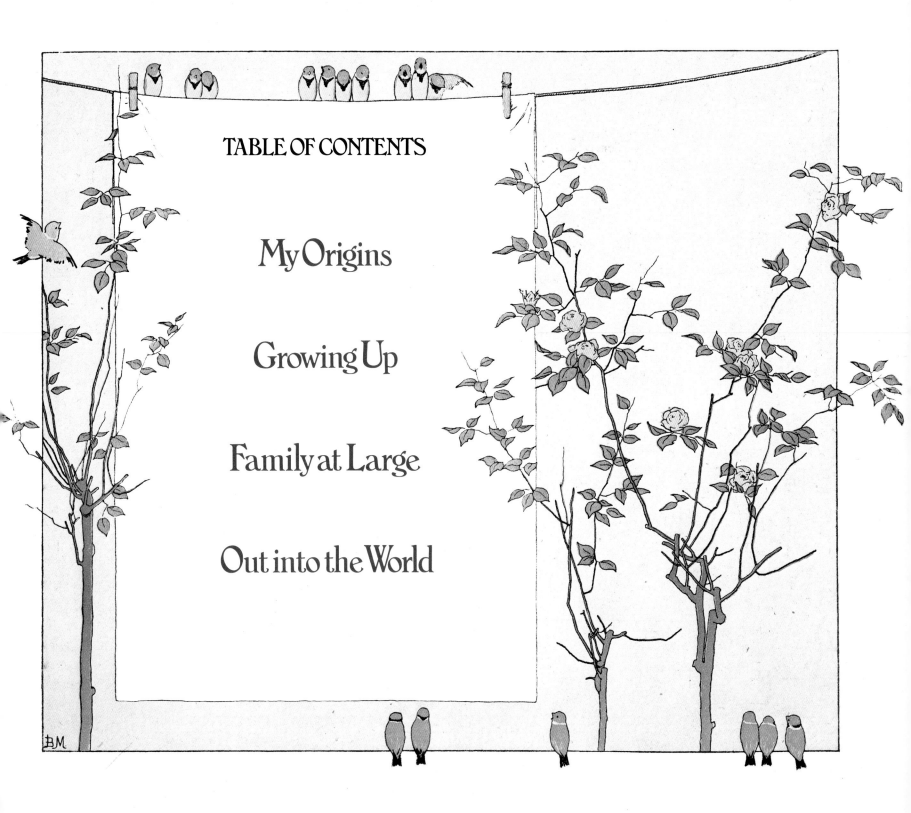

TABLE OF CONTENTS

My Origins

Where did you come from, baby dear?
Out of the everywhere into here.
GEORGE MACDONALD

WHEN I WAS A BABY

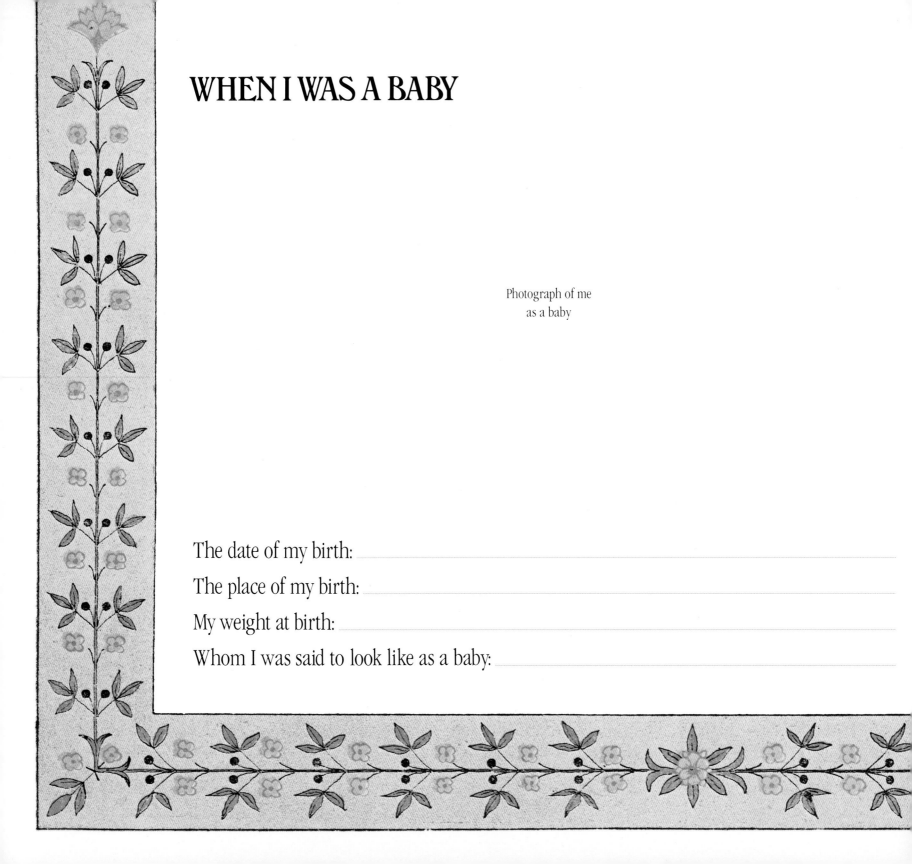

Photograph of me
as a baby

The date of my birth: _____

The place of my birth: _____

My weight at birth: _____

Whom I was said to look like as a baby: _____

My first memories:

That age is best which is the first....
ROBERT HERRICK

MY PARENTS

My mother's full name: ....

The date of her birth: ....

The place of her birth: ....

....

....

My father's full name: ....

The date of his birth: ....

The place of his birth: ....

....

Thyself hast called me by my name....
CHARLES WESLEY

How and when my parents met:

The date of my parents' wedding:

Their occupations:

How my mother used to enjoy spending her free time: _____

_____

_____

_____

_____

_____

How my father used to enjoy spending his free time: _____

_____

_____

_____

_____

_____

_____

Special memories of my parents:

MY GRANDPARENTS

On my mother's side

My grandfather's name: _____

The date of his birth: _____

The place of his birth: _____

My grandmother's name: _____

The date of her birth: _____

The place of her birth: _____

On my father's side

My grandfather's name: _____

The date of his birth: _____

The place of his birth: _____

My grandmother's name: _____

The date of her birth: _____

The place of her birth: _____

Dear days of old, with the faces in the firelight....
ROBERT LOUIS STEVENSON

Where my grandparents lived:

Their occupations:

Special memories of my grandparents:

PHOTOGRAPHS OF MY PARENTS AND GRANDPARENTS

Photo

Photo

Name:
Relation:

Name:
Relation:

Photo

Photo

Name:
Relation:

Name:
Relation:

Growing Up

Everybody wants to be somebody;
nobody wants to grow.
GOETHE

LIFE AT HOME

As a child I lived at:

The rest of the family comprised:

What was expected of me; the things that were strictly forbidden:

I remember, I remember,
The house where I was born....
THOMAS HOOD

Our neighbors:

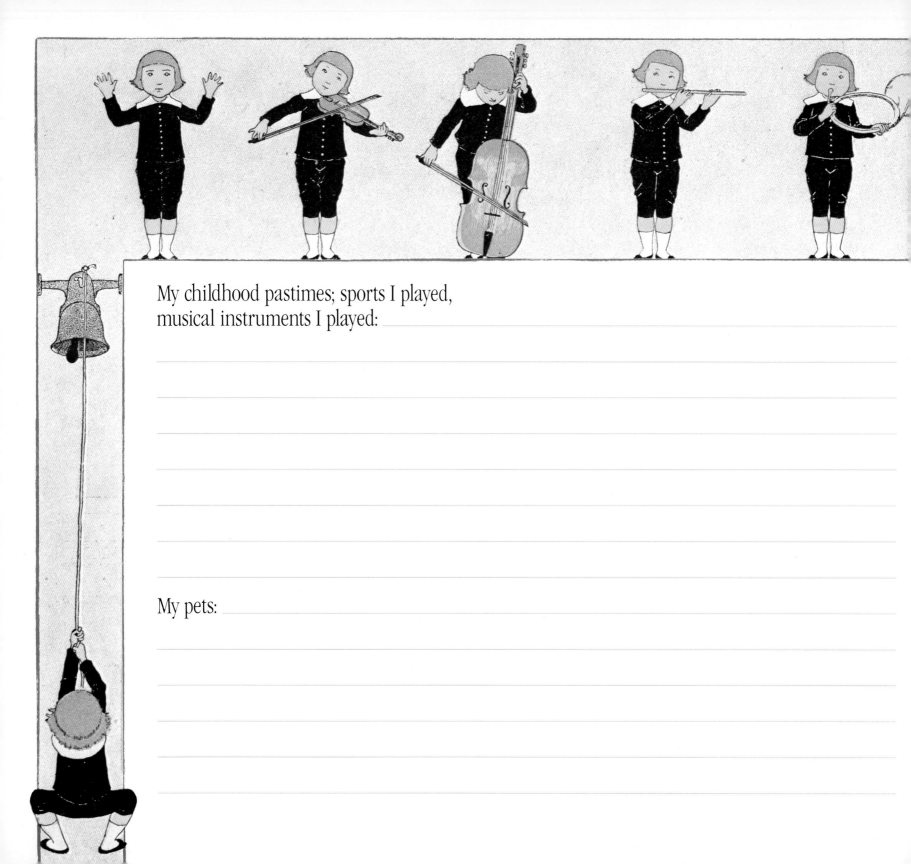

My childhood pastimes; sports I played,
musical instruments I played:

My pets:

Birthday parties I remember:

SCHOOL DAYS

Where I went to school; how I got there each day:

I have had playmates, I have had companions,
In my days of childhood, in my joyful school-days....
CHARLES LAMB

Teachers and school friends I remember:

FAMILY HOLIDAYS

Who went; where we went; memories of special holidays:

I sing of brooks, of blossoms, birds, and bowers,
Of April, May, of June, and July flowers.
ROBERT HERRICK

MORE MEMORIES OF MY CHILDHOOD AND TEENAGE YEARS

How I most enjoyed spending my time; what I most feared;
my special friends; favorite books, songs, food:

In youth is pleasure, in youth is pleasure.
ROBERT WEVER

DATING AND ROMANCE

What I remember of my first date; my parents' advice about dating; where
I met the person I married; what was the rage in music, dance, clothes:

Youth's the season made for joys,
Love is then our duty....
JOHN GAY

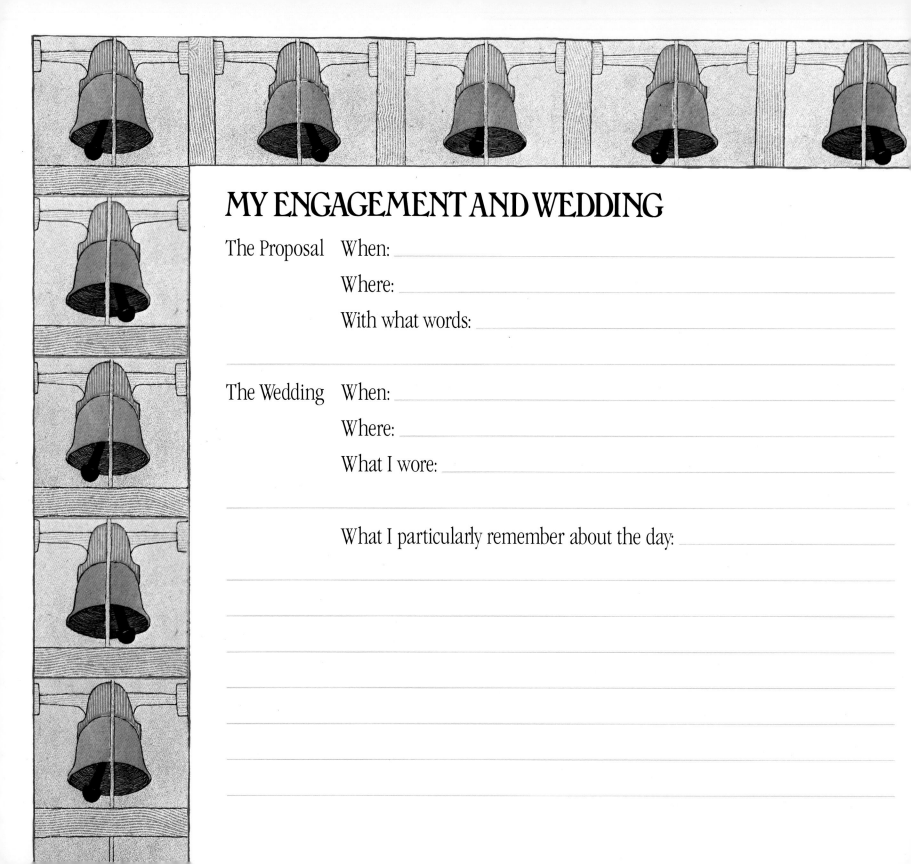

MY ENGAGEMENT AND WEDDING

The Proposal   When: _____

Where: _____

With what words: _____

The Wedding   When: _____

Where: _____

What I wore: _____

What I particularly remember about the day: _____

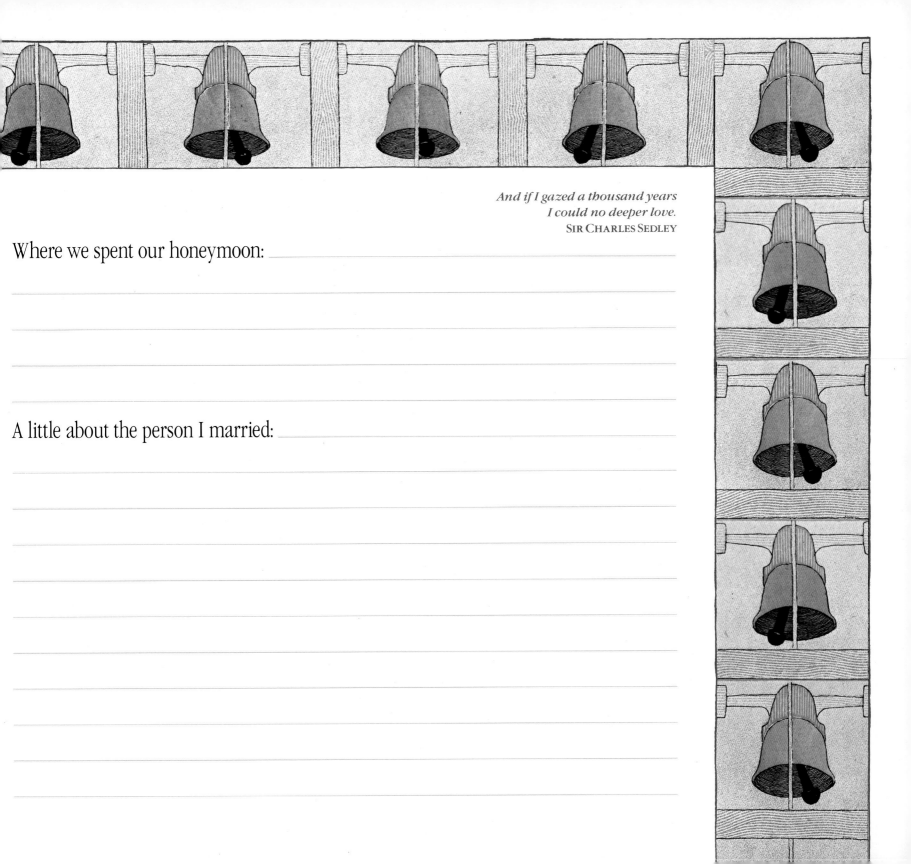

And if I gazed a thousand years
I could no deeper love.
Sir Charles Sedley

Where we spent our honeymoon:

A little about the person I married:

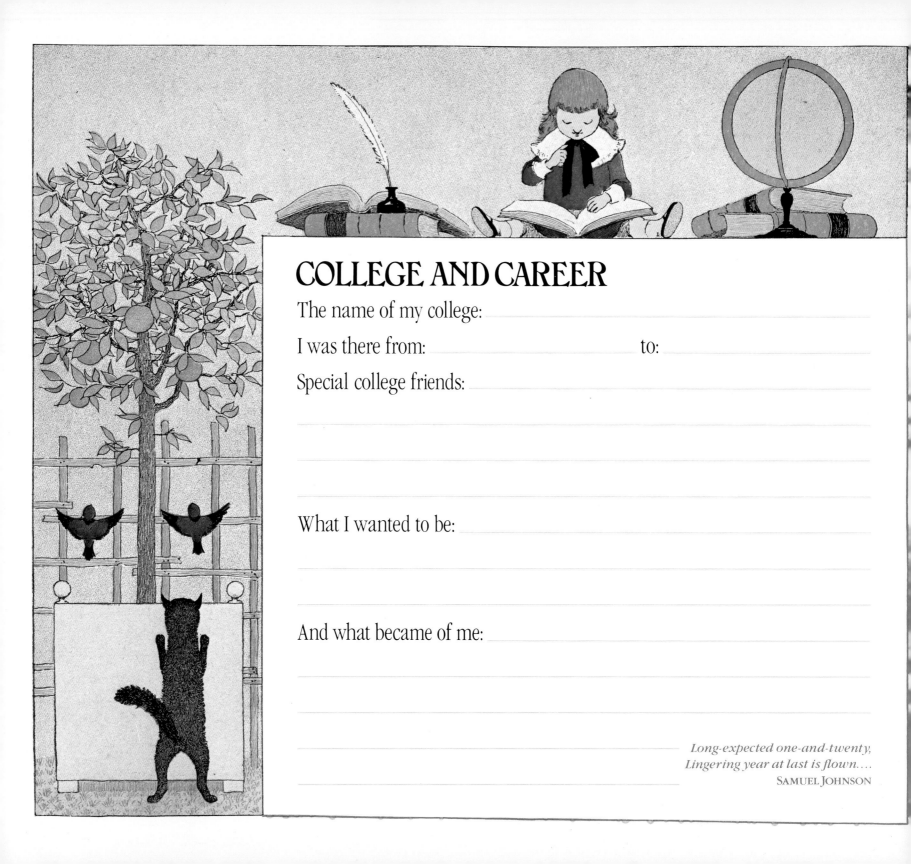

COLLEGE AND CAREER

The name of my college: _____

I was there from: _____ to: _____

Special college friends: _____

_____

_____

What I wanted to be: _____

_____

And what became of me: _____

_____

_____

Long-expected one-and-twenty,
Lingering year at last is flown....
SAMUEL JOHNSON

Family at Large

Visit your aunt, but not every day; and call at your brother's, but not every night.
BENJAMIN FRANKLIN

THE FAMILY TREE

Relatives I remember from my mother's side of the family;
where they lived; our first meeting; when I last saw them: _____

_____

_____

_____

_____

_____

_____

Relatives I remember from my father's side of the family;
where they lived; our first meeting; when I last saw them: _____

_____

_____

_____

_____

_____

_____

FAMILY FACES AND FORTUNES

How you might have recognized a member of my family:

Occupations and careers my relatives chose:

There is a divinity that shapes our ends,
Rough-hew them how we will.
WILLIAM SHAKESPEARE

Where different members of the family have settled;
news of uncles, aunts, brothers, sisters, cousins:

FAMILY TRADITIONS

At mealtimes; for Thanksgiving, July 4:

Special family occasions I remember:

Imagination fondly stoops to trace
The parlor splendors of that festive place....
OLIVER GOLDSMITH

FAMILY JOKES, FAMILY FOLKLORE

He knew an hundred pleasant stories....
JONATHAN SWIFT

The real characters in the family; those I met,
those I heard about:

PHOTOGRAPHS OF THE FAMILY AT LARGE

Photo

Photo

Name:
Relation:

Name:
Relation:

Photo

Photo

Name:
Relation:

Name:
Relation:

Out into the World

Only so much do I know, as I have lived.
RALPH WALDO EMERSON

MY TRAVELS

The places that I have visited; the places where I have lived:

I travelled among unknown men,
In lands beyond the sea....
WILLIAM WORDSWORTH

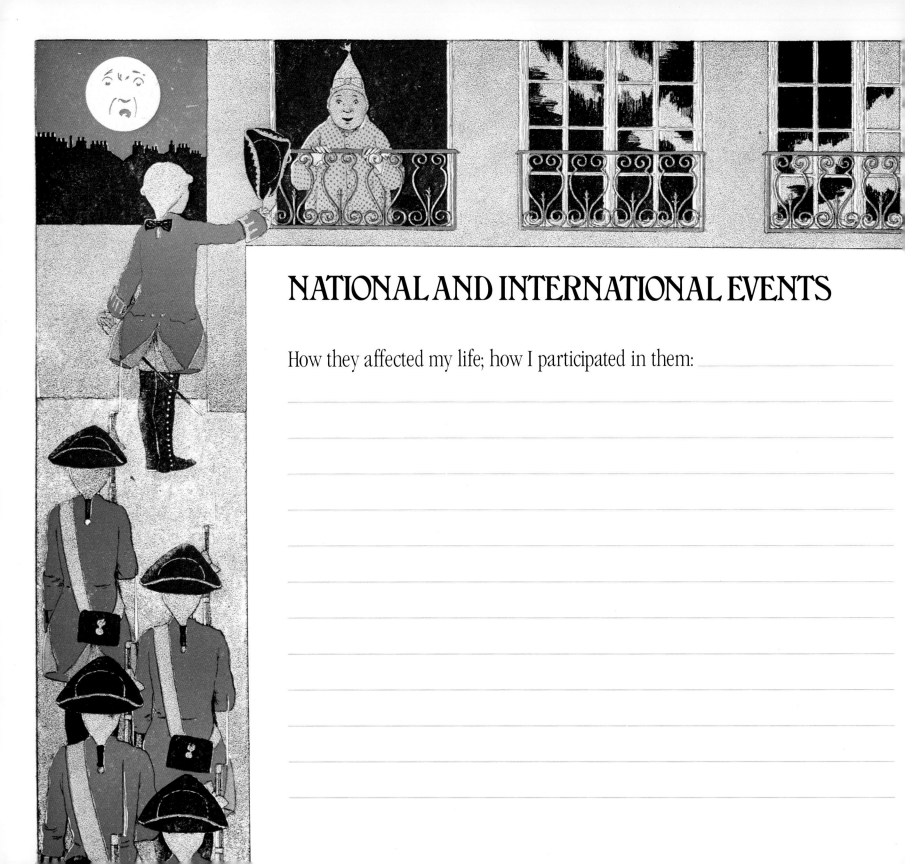

NATIONAL AND INTERNATIONAL EVENTS

How they affected my life; how I participated in them:

A piper in the streets to-day
Set up, and tuned, and started to play,
And away, away, away on the tide
Of his music we started....
SEUMAS O'SULLIVAN

SUCCESSES AND FAILURES

My greatest achievements: _____

_____

_____

_____

_____

_____

_____

The most difficult times I have had to go through: _____

_____

_____

_____

_____

_____

One crowded hour of glorious life
Is worth an age without a name.
THOMAS OSBERT MORDAUNT

What I most regret:

My happiest memories:

REFLECTIONS

Those who have most influenced me during my life:

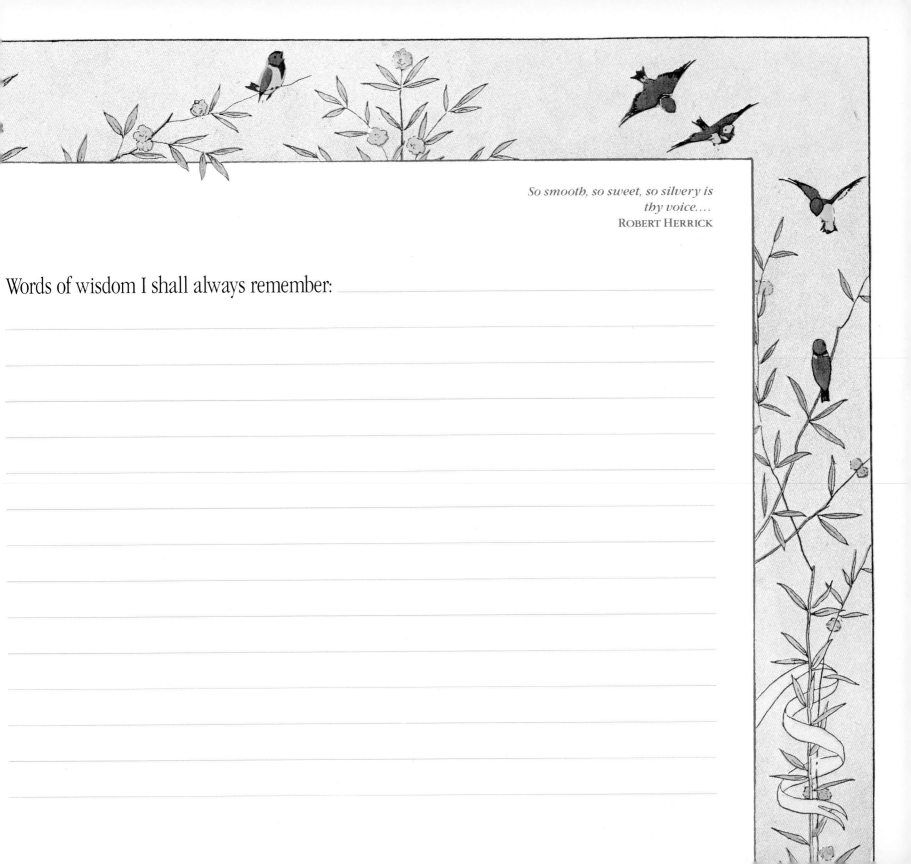

So smooth, so sweet, so silvery is
thy voice....
ROBERT HERRICK

Words of wisdom I shall always remember:

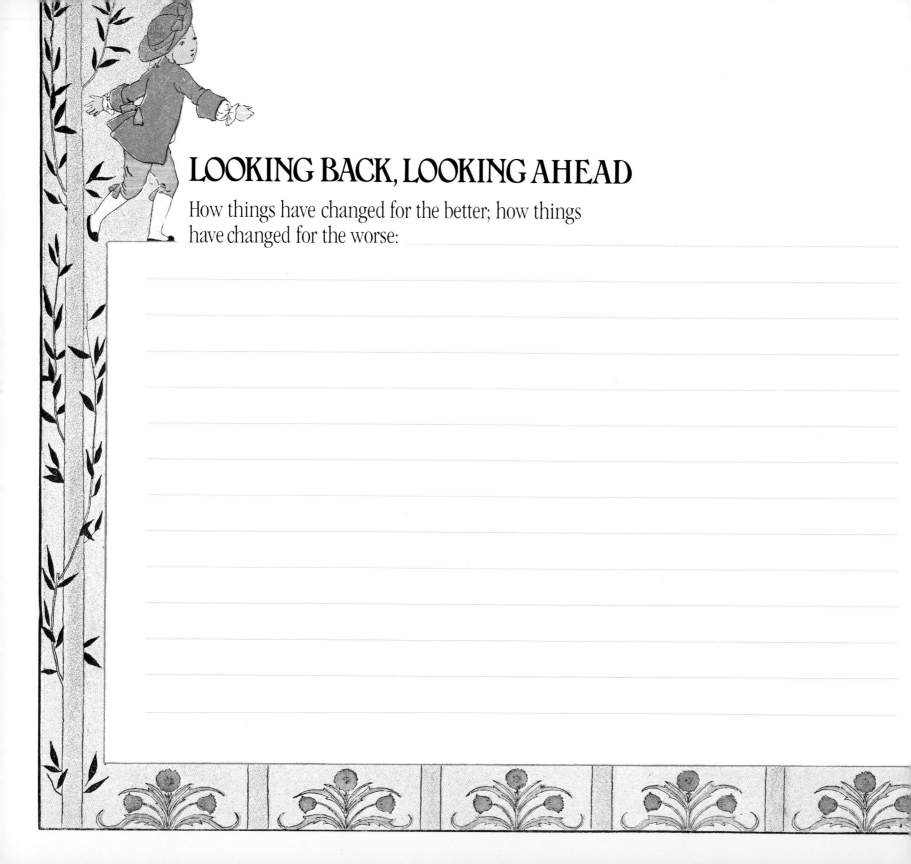

LOOKING BACK, LOOKING AHEAD

How things have changed for the better; how things
have changed for the worse:

If there were dreams to sell,
What would you buy?
THOMAS LOVELL BEDDOES

My hopes for the future:

A FEW WORDS OF ADVICE

I love the fond,
The faithful, young, and true.
JOHN CLARE